SCHOLASTIC

SATs Made Simple

Algebra

Ages 10-11

Generalise Rule Puzzle

Formulae x Pattern

$a = b + c$

Linear 16-a=7 Expression

Symbol Equation

$\frac{1}{3}$ Sequence

Integer $+$

y Enumerate

Formula Pattern

SCHOLASTIC

Published in the UK by Scholastic Education, 2021

Book End, Range Road, Witney, Oxfordshire, OX29 0YD

A division of Scholastic Limited

London – New York – Toronto – Sydney – Auckland

Mexico City – New Delhi – Hong Kong

© 2021 Scholastic Limited

123456789   1234567890

A British Library Cataloguing-in-Publication Data
A catalogue record for this book is available from the British Library.

ISBN 978-1407-18382-4
Printed and bound by Ashford Colour Press

Author

Giles Clare

Editorial team

Robin Hunt, Rachel Morgan, Kate Baxter, Tracy Kewley, David and Jackie Link

Design team

Andrea Lewis

Illustration

QBS Learning

Contents

The answers can be found online at: **www.scholastic.co.uk/sats-algebra**

How to use this book

This book provides you with a step-by-step guide to all aspects of algebra, providing a complete route to mastery of this vital area of the National Curriculum for mathematics at Key Stage 2.

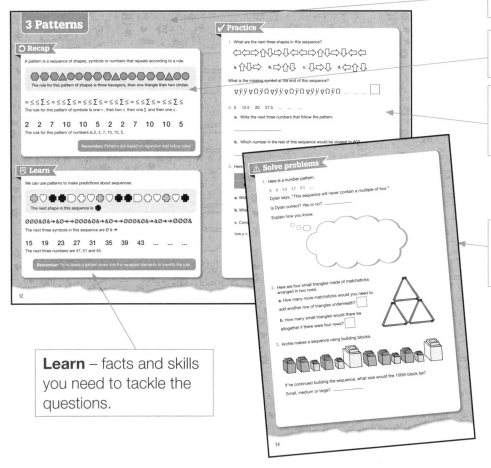

Title – there are 12 units in total and two practice tests.

Recap – review what you should have learned already.

Practice – practise what you have learned with arithmetic-style questions.

Solve problems – these will be similar to those you may get in your SATs test.

Learn – facts and skills you need to tackle the questions.

At the end of the book are two practice tests which provide questions similar to those you may get in your SATs test.

A handy progress chart on page 5 allows you to track your understanding. It is a good idea to tick off a section only when all of the questions have been completed correctly, with mistakes corrected and any misunderstandings clarified.

There is a useful glossary at the back of the book, and answers are available online at: **www.scholastic.co.uk/sats-algebra**

Progress chart

Making progress? Tick (✔) the circles as you complete each unit of the book.

Work through one unit at a time before moving on to the next one.

1 Equivalence ○ ── **2** Order of operations ○

3

○ **4** Linear number sequences ── ○ Patterns

5 Non-linear number sequences ○ ── **6** Missing numbers ○

7

○ **8** More equations ── ○ Equations

9

Equations (two unknowns) ○ ── **10** Possible numbers ○

11

○ **12** Algebraic formulae ── ○ Word formulae

13

Practice test – Arithmetic ○ ── **14** Practice test – Reasoning ○

Well done!

1 Equivalence

The equals sign '=' is often used to mean 'makes'.

5 + 3 = 8	'Five plus three makes eight.'
20 − 14 = 6	'Twenty take away fourteen makes six.'
6 × 4 = 24	'Six times four makes twenty-four.'
72 ÷ 8 = 9	'Seventy-two divided by eight makes nine.'

We can use the equals sign to mean 'makes' with simple calculations like this.

📄 Learn

Did you know you can write all those calculations another way? Here, using the word 'makes' doesn't make sense.

8 = 5 + 3	'Eight makes five plus three.'
6 = 20 − 14	'Six makes twenty take away fourteen.'
24 = 6 × 4	'Twenty-four makes six times four.'
9 = 72 ÷ 8	'Nine makes seventy-two divided by eight.'

The equals sign means 'is the same as' or 'is equivalent to'. Think of it as the point of balance in a calculation.

Remember: The equals sign means more than 'makes'. This is especially important in algebra.

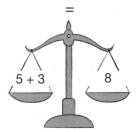

You can have more than one number on each side of the equals sign. In algebra you also use letters to show variables or unknown numbers. These are known as 'equations'.

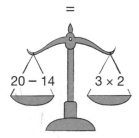
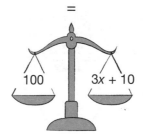
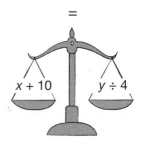

1. Write in the missing numbers to balance the values on each side of the scales.

   a.   =

   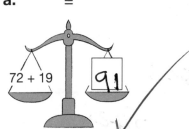

   72 + 19 | 91 ✓

   b.   =

   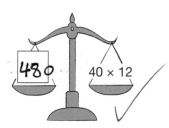

   480 | 40 × 12 ✓

   c.   =

   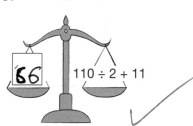

   66 | 110 ÷ 2 + 11 ✓

2. Write in the missing numbers to balance the values on each side of the equals sign.

   a. 30 × 4 = ☐120 ✓

   b. ☐100 = 80 + 20 ✓

   c. ☐52 = 12 × 2 + 28 ✓

   Write in the missing numbers. One has been done for you.

   d.   =

   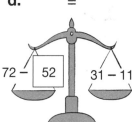

   72 − ☐52 | 31 − 11

   e.   = 150

   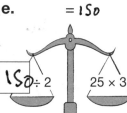

   150 ÷ 2 | 25 × 3 ✓

   f.   =

   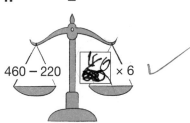

   460 − 220 | ☐40 × 6 ✓

3. Rewrite each equation another way so that it remains equivalent.
   One has been done for you.

   a. 14 × 70 = 980   980 = 14 × 70

   b. 19 = 31 − 12   12 + 19 = 31 ✓

   c. 20 × 5 = 200 ÷ 2   200 ÷ 5 = 20 × 2 ✓

   d. x = 750 − 250   250 + x = 750 ✓

   e. y + 11 = x − 8   x − 8 = y + 11 ✓

   Good ☺

⚠ Solve problems

1. Two farmers each have the same number of sheep.

   The first farmer has ten fields. He keeps 32 sheep in each field.

   The second farmer has eight fields. She keeps 40 sheep in each field.

   a. Write this as a balanced equation. $32 \times 10 = 40 \times 8$ ✓

   b. How many sheep do the farmers have altogether? _____ 640 _____ sheep ✓

2. Lola thinks of a number.

   She says, "When I multiply my number by four and then subtract 11 the answer is 17."

   Write Lola's sentence as a balanced equation using the letter x to show the number she is thinking of.

   _____ $7x \ 4 \ -11 = 17$ _____ ✓

3. Use these numbers to balance the scales.

   21   22   24   25

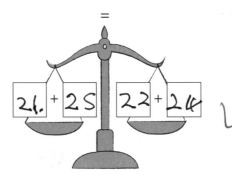

   $21 + 25 \quad 22 + 24$ ✓

4. Meg and Luca are discussing this equation:

   $5x + 15 = \cancel{\cancel{y}}^{30} - 10$

   Meg says, "I think you can rewrite the equation as $y - 10 = x + 15$."

   Luca says, "I think you can rewrite the equation as $y + 15 = x - 10$."

   Who is correct? Meg or Luca? _____ Meg _____

   Explain why.

   because Meg turned it around.

   Well done Ang

   3wp

Mrs McFarlan

2 Order of operations

◯ **Recap** ◅

When we talk about operations in maths, we mean addition, subtraction, multiplication and division. We can use these operations with any type of number (integers, decimals and fractions).

📄 Learn ◅

We can use more than one operation in a calculation. However, you must do those operations in a special order known as BIDMAS.

> **BIDMAS** is a good way of remembering the order in which you should do the operations. It stands for:
>
> **B** rackets — Do any calculation within brackets ( ) first.
>
> **I** ndices — Do the square (x^2) or cube (x^3) numbers next.
>
> $\left\{ \begin{array}{l} \textbf{D} \text{ ivision} \\ \textbf{M} \text{ ultiplication} \end{array} \right\}$ — Then do the division (÷) or… …the multiplication (×).
>
> $\left\{ \begin{array}{l} \textbf{A} \text{ ddition} \\ \textbf{S} \text{ ubtraction} \end{array} \right\}$ — Then do the addition (+) or… …the subtraction (–).

If you don't use this BIDMAS order, your answers will be incorrect.
Look at the difference when you use BIDMAS and when you don't.

Using BIDMAS	Not using BIDMAS
$12 - 3 \times 2 = 6$ ✔ You must multiply before you subtract.	$12 - 3 \times 2 = 18$ ✘ If you do $12 - 3 = 9$ and then $9 \times 2 = 18$
$5 \times (20 + 30) = 250$ ✔ You must do the addition in the brackets before you multiply. So, $20 + 30 = 50$ and then $5 \times 50 = 250$	$5 \times (20 + 30) = 130$ ✘ If you do $5 \times 20 = 100$ and then $100 + 30 = 130$
$6 + 5^2 = 31$ ✔ You must square the 5 before you add. So, $5^2 = 25$ and then $6 + 25 = 31$	$6 + 5^2 = 121$ ✘ If you do $6 + 5 = 11$ and then $11^2 = 121$

> **Remember:** Division and multiplication rank equally in BIDMAS so just calculate them from left to right, whichever operation comes first. The same is true for addition and subtraction.

1. Underline the part of the calculation that you should do first. One is done for you.

   a. 75 − $\underline{5 \times 5}$ **b.** 8 × $\underline{(21 - 14)}$ **c.** 54 ÷ $\underline{3^2}$ **d.** $\underline{(40 \times 2)}$ + 120   **e.** $\underline{3 \times 12}$ ÷ 4

2. Now write the answers to each of the calculations in Question 1.

   a. 50   **b.** 56   **c.** 6

   d. 200   **e.** 9

3. Label the parts of the calculation in the order in which you should do them. One is done for you.

   a. $\overset{\text{1st}}{\overbrace{500}} \div \underset{\text{2nd}}{\underbrace{10^2}} + \underset{\text{3rd}}{\underbrace{15}}$

   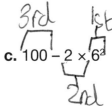

   b. $12 + (5 + 2) \times 9$ (1st, 2nd over (5+2) × 9; 3rd below)

   c. $100 - 2 \times 6^2$ (3rd, 1st over 2 × 6²; 2nd below)

4. Now write the answers to each of the calculations in Question 3.

   a. 20   **b.** 75   **c.** 28

5. Write T (true) or F (false) for each of these calculations.

   a. 60 ÷ 10 + 2 = 5 [F]   **b.** 9 × (20 − 12) = 168 [F]   **c.** $5^2 - (4 \times 3) = 13$ [T]

   d. $3^2 + 7^2 \times 2 = 107$ [T]   **e.** 12 × 11 ÷ 3 = 44 [T]

6. Calculate the following.

   a. 6 + 6 × 6 = _____

   b. $(84 - 3) \div 3^2$ = _____

   c. (12 + 13) × (40 ÷ 8) = _____

   d. 160 − (20 − 9) × 10 = _____

   e. $3^2 + (7 + 2)^2$ = _____

1. Marlon has written some calculations. He has left out the operations. Add the operations so that the calculations are correct.

   a. 10 ☐ 2 ☐ 2 = 3

   b. 3 ☐ (4 ☐ 2) = 18

   c. 15 ☐ 3 ☐ 2 = 9

2. Harry buys two pairs of shorts and three T-shirts.

   How much change does he receive from a £20 note?

£3.50   £2.50

   £ ☐

3. Ava has drawn a straight line on a graph. She says, "I notice that the *y* coordinate is always eight less than the *x* coordinate."

   a. Write the equation for the line that Ava has drawn. _____

   b. What is the *y* coordinate if the *x* coordinate is 5? (5, ___)

3 Patterns

A pattern is a sequence of shapes, symbols or numbers that repeats according to a rule.

The rule for this pattern of shapes is three hexagons, then one triangle then two circles.

$\approx \leq \leq \sum \leq \approx \leq \leq \sum \leq \approx \leq \leq \sum \leq \approx \leq \leq \sum \leq \approx \leq \leq \sum \leq \approx \leq \leq \sum \leq$

The rule for this pattern of symbols is one $\approx$, then two $\leq$, then one $\sum$ and then one $\leq$.

| 2 | 2 | 7 | 10 | 10 | 5 | 2 | 2 | 7 | 10 | 10 | 5 |

The rule for this pattern of numbers is 2, 2, 7, 10, 10, 5.

Remember: Patterns are based on repetition and follow rules.

📄 Learn

We can use patterns to make predictions about sequences.

The next shape in this sequence is 🛡️

$\emptyset\emptyset\emptyset\&\emptyset\&\Rightarrow\&\emptyset\Rightarrow\Rightarrow\emptyset\emptyset\emptyset\&\emptyset\&\Rightarrow\&\emptyset\Rightarrow\Rightarrow\emptyset\emptyset\emptyset\&\emptyset\&\Rightarrow\&\emptyset\Rightarrow\Rightarrow\emptyset\emptyset\emptyset\&$

The next three symbols in this sequence are $\emptyset$ & $\Rightarrow$

| 15 | 19 | 23 | 27 | 31 | 35 | 39 | 43 | ... | ... | ... |

The next three numbers are 47, 51 and 55.

Remember: Try to break a pattern down into the repeated elements or identify the rule.

1. What are the next three shapes in this sequence?

   a. ⇧⇩⇨   b. ⇨⇧⇩   c. ⇩⇨⇩   d. ⇦⇧⇩

2. What is the missing symbol at the end of this sequence?

   ∇ÿÿ ∇Ωÿ Ω ∇ÿÿ ∇Ωÿ Ω ∇ÿÿ ∇Ωÿ Ω …   …   …   ☐

3. 5   12.5   20   27.5   …   …   …

   a. Write the next three numbers that follow the pattern.

   _____

   b. Which number in the rest of this sequence would be closest to 60?

   _____

4. Here are two number patterns.

Row x	2	4	6	8
Row y	7	13	19	25

   a. Which number will come next in row x? _____

   b. Which number will come next in row y? _____

   c. Complete the rule for the number pattern for the number pairs in the columns.

   Row y = Row x × ☐ + ☐

1. Here is a number pattern.

   5 9 13 17 21 ...

   Dylan says, "This sequence will never contain a multiple of four."

   Is Dylan correct? Yes or no? _____

   Explain how you know.

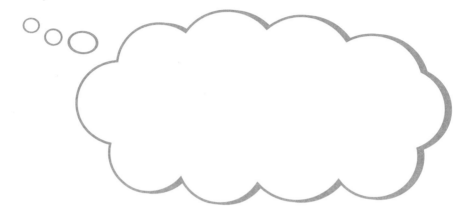

2. Here are four small triangles made of matchsticks arranged in two rows.

   a. How many more matchsticks would you need to add another row of triangles underneath? ☐

   b. How many small triangles would there be altogether if there were four rows? ☐

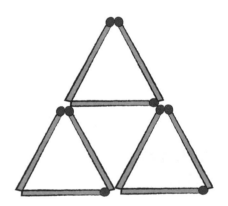

3. Archie makes a sequence using building blocks.

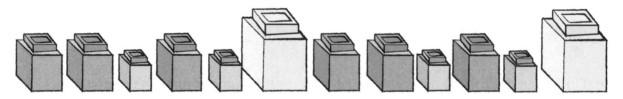

   If he continued building the sequence, what size would the 100th block be?

   Small, medium or large? _____

4 Linear number sequences

A number sequence is a type of pattern. The numbers in the sequence follow a rule.

The rule for this sequence is 'Add 4.'

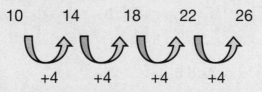

📄 Learn

There are two types of number sequence: linear sequences and non-linear sequences.

In a linear number sequence, the difference between the numbers stays the same. The rule may involve adding or subtracting by the same amount each time.

The rule for this linear sequence is 'Add 0.5'.

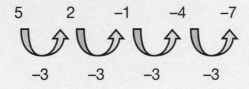

The rule for this linear sequence is 'Subtract 3'.

5   2   −1   −4   −7
−3   −3   −3   −3

Remember: You need to work out the difference between each number in the sequence to work out the rule.

1. Complete these linear sequences.

   a. The rule for this sequence is 'Add 12'.

   8   20   32   ☐   ☐   ☐

   b. The rule for this sequence is 'Subtract 2.1'.

   19.5   17.4   ☐   ☐   ☐   ☐

   c. The rule for this sequence is 'Add 6'.

   −10   −4   ☐   ☐   ☐   ☐

   d. The rule for this sequence is 'Subtract 100'.

   1363   1263   1163   ☐   ☐   ☐

2. Complete these linear sequences and write the rule.

   a. 0.3   0.7   1.1   ☐   ☐   ☐

   The rule for this sequence is _____.

   b. 98   87   76   ☐   ☐   ☐

   The rule for this sequence is _____.

   c. 66   78   90   ☐   ☐   ☐

   The rule for this sequence is _____.

   d. 12.5   10   7.5   ☐   ☐   ☐

   The rule for this sequence is _____.

⚠ Solve problems

1. The numbers in this sequence increase by 32 each time. Write in the two missing numbers.

   [ ]   56   88   120   [ ]

2. Complete the linear sequences in these grids. The sequences run horizontally and vertically.

   a.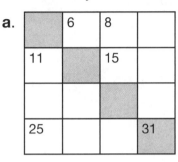

   b. What is the rule for the horizontal sequences?

   _____

   c. What is the rule for the vertical sequences?

   _____

   d. Write out the rule for the shaded squares from the top left to the bottom right of

   the grid. _____

3. The numbers in this sequence decrease by 0.6 each time.

   3.8   3.2   2.6   2 ...

   Which number in the sequence will be closest to zero? _____

4. Ethan and Lena are discussing this linear number sequence:

   −3   −12   −21   −30 ...

   Ethan says, "I think the rule for this sequence is subtract 9."

   Lena disagrees and says, "I think the rule for this sequence is add 9."

   Who is correct? Ethan or Lena?

   _____

   Explain why.

5 Non-linear number sequences

↻ **Recap**

In a linear number sequence, the difference between the numbers stays the same. The rule may involve adding or subtracting by the same amount each time.

The rule for this linear sequence is 'Subtract 7'.

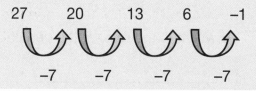

27   20   13   6   −1

−7   −7   −7   −7

Learn

Some number sequences are not linear. In a non-linear sequence, the difference between each number changes. This happens when you multiply or divide.

The rule for this non-linear sequence is 'Multiply by 3'.

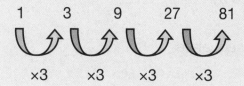

1   3   9   27   81

×3   ×3   ×3   ×3

The rule for this non-linear sequence is 'Halve it' or 'Divide by 2'.

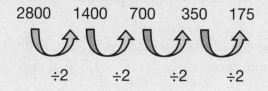

2800   1400   700   350   175

÷2   ÷2   ÷2   ÷2

Some non-linear sequences have rules that involve more than one operation.

The rule for this non-linear sequence is 'Multiply by 2 and add 10'.

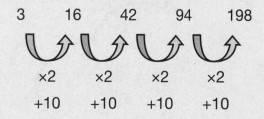

3   16   42   94   198

×2   ×2   ×2   ×2
+10   +10   +10   +10

The rule for this non-linear sequence is 'The first difference is +5 and then the difference increases by 2 each time'.

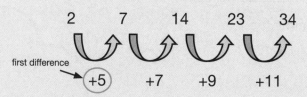

2   7   14   23   34

first difference → +5   +7   +9   +11

Remember: These sequences still follow a rule. Work out the difference to work out the rule.

1. **a.** The rule for this sequence is 'Double it'. 2.5 ☐ ☐ ☐ ☐ ☐

   b. The rule for this sequence is 'Divide by 10'. 140 14 1.4 ☐ ☐ ☐

   c. The rule for this sequence is 'Multiply by 3 and subtract 5'. Complete the sequence.

   3 4 7 ☐ ☐ ☐

   d. The rule for this sequence is 'Subtract 11 and double it'. Complete the sequence.

   24 26 ☐ ☐ ☐ ☐

2. **a.** Complete this sequence and then complete the rule.

   0.58 5.8 58 ☐ ☐ ☐

   The rule for this sequence is _____.

   b. Complete this sequence and then complete the rule. The rule involves two operations.

   37 21 13 9 ☐ ☐

   The rule is 'Add _____ and divide by _____'.

3. **a.** Complete this sequence by writing in the difference between the numbers.

   The rule is 'The first difference is +1. The difference increases by 1 each time'.

   2   3   5   8   ☐ ☐

   | +1 | +2 | + | + | + |

   b. Complete this sequence by writing in the difference between the numbers.

   The rule is 'The first difference is −4. The difference increases by 2 each time'.

   10   6   0   -8   ☐ ☐

   | −4 | −6 | − | − | − |

4. Complete the rule for this sequence.

   11   21   34   50   69   91

   The rule is: 'The first difference is _____. The difference increases by _____ each time'.

⚠ Solve problems

1. The rule for this sequence is 'Add 3 and multiply by 10'. Write in the missing numbers.

    ☐   90   930   ☐   93,330

2. Here is a non-linear sequence. The difference increases by the same amount each time. Write in the missing numbers.

    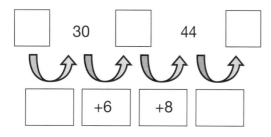

    ☐   30   ☐   44   ☐

    ☐   +6   +8   ☐

3. The rule for this sequence is 'Double it and add 2'.

    2   6   14   _____

    Write two numbers from the sequence that add to make a total of 140.

    ☐   and   ☐

4. Here is part of a 100 square. Some numbers have been circled according to this rule:

    'The first difference is +2. The difference then doubles each time'.

1	2	3	4	5	6	7	8	9	10
11	12	13	14	15	16	17	18	19	20
21	22	23	24	25	26	27	28	29	30
31	32	33	34	35	36	37	38	39	40

    Circle the next number in the sequence on the 100 square.

6 Missing numbers

↺ **Recap**

In any calculation question, there is always a missing number: the answer! This missing number is usually at the end of the calculation.

$7 + 9 = ?$ $18 - 13 = ?$

$8 \times 6 = ?$ $28 \div 4 = ?$

$? = 7 + 9$ $? = 18 - 13$

$? = 8 \times 6$ $? = 28 \div 4$

We know from Unit 1 Equivalence that these calculations can also be written another way, by putting the missing number at the start of the calculation.

📄 Learn

The missing number can in fact be anywhere in a calculation. The missing number may be a box to write in.

Example:

$7 + \boxed{} = 16$ Here the missing number is in the middle of the calculation.

You can work out the value of the missing number by using what you already know.

$7 + \boxed{} = 16$ You know $16 - 7 = 9$, so the number in the box must be $\boxed{9}$.

The missing number may also be represented by a symbol.

$⬡ - 13 = 5$ $48 = \triangle \times 6$ $7 = 28 \div \bigcirc$

You can work out the values of the missing numbers in the same way.

$⬡ - 13 = 5$ You know that $5 + 13 = 18$, so $⬡$ must be 18.

$48 = \triangle \times 6$ You know that $48 \div 6 = 8$, so $\triangle$ must be 8.

$7 = 28 \div \bigcirc$ You know that $28 \div 7 = 4$, so $\bigcirc$ must be 4.

Remember: Knowing your times tables thoroughly is important for this type of question.

1. Write the missing numbers in the boxes.

   a. ☐ + 12 = 25

   b. 14 + ☐ = 50

   c. ☐ + 80 = 120

   d. 22 − ☐ = 14

   e. ☐ − 60 = 90

   f. 75 = ☐ − 25

2. Write the missing numbers in the boxes.

   a. 9 × ☐ = 720

   b. ☐ × 3 = 63

   c. 360 = ☐ × 60

   d. ☐ ÷ 11 = 11

   e. 13 = 39 ÷ ☐

   f. 240 ÷ ☐ = 4

3. Write the value of the symbols.

   a. 19 + ⬡ = 49

   ⬡ =

   b. △ − 9 = 82

   △ =

   c. 80 = 4 × ⬭

   ⬭ =

   d. ▱ ÷ 50 = 5

   ▱ =

1. Write in the four missing numbers.

7	=		−	
×		=		×
		4		5
=		+		=
21	−	6	=	

2. The missing number in this equation is 27.5.

$2.5 = \boxed{} \div 11$ 　　　　True or false? _____

Explain why by showing your working.

3. Write down the values of the symbols in this puzzle.

	▭			
96	−	◣	=	44
	29			÷
16.8	=	⬠	×	4
	4			=
				▱

▭ = ☐　　　◣ = ☐　　　⬠ = ☐　　　▱ = ☐

4. Jasmina is working out the value of the symbol in this equation:

$42 + \hexagon = 58$

She says, "I know I can add 58 and 42 and that will give the answer. The symbol represents 100."

Is Jasmina correct? Yes or no? _____

　　　　　　Explain why.

7 Equations

Equations have two sides separated by an equals sign. Think of equations as scales that must balance. The values on the left-hand side of an equation must always be equal to the values on the right-hand side.

$$10 + 30 = 40$$
$$30 + 10 = 20 + 20$$
$$40 = 50 - 10$$

Where there is a missing number in an equation, we can use boxes or symbols to represent the missing number.

$$10 + \square = 40$$
$$30 + 10 = \hexagon + 20$$
$$\triangle = 50 - 10$$

📄 Learn

In algebra, instead of boxes or symbols, we use letters to represent missing numbers.

$$x + 9 = 16 \qquad y - 14 = 15$$

You can work out the value of the letters. This is known as 'solving the equation'.

There are special ways to write algebra when using multiplication and division.

$a \times 12 = 60$ is written as $12a = 60$

$b \div 4 = 10$ is written as $\frac{b}{4} = 10$

Remember: If you do something to one side of an equation, you must do the same thing to the other side to balance it out.

$x + \cancel{9} = 16$ $^{-9}$	To calculate x, start by subtracting 9 from the left-hand side of the equation.
$x = 16 - 9$	This means you must subtract 9 from the right-hand side too.
$x = 7$	Complete the calculation to solve the equation: x is 7.

$\cancel{12}a = 60$ $^{\div 12}$	To calculate a, start by dividing the left-hand side of the equation by 12.
$a = 60 \div 12$	This means you must divide the right-hand side by 12 too.
$a = 5$	Complete the calculation to solve the equation: a is 5.

$y - \cancel{14} = 15$ $^{+14}$	To calculate y, start by adding 14 to the left-hand side of the equation.
$y = 15 + 14$	This means you must add 14 to the right-hand side too.
$y = 29$	Complete the calculation to solve the equation: y is 29.

$\frac{b}{\cancel{4}} = 10$ $^{\times 4}$	To calculate b, start by multiplying the left-hand side of the equation by 4.
$b = 10 \times 4$	This means you must multiply the right-hand side by 4 too.
$b = 40$	Complete the calculation to solve the equation: b is 40.

1. Write the missing numbers in the boxes.

a. $a + 9 = 27$

$a =$ ☐

b. $b - 23 = 44$

$b =$ ☐

c. $9x = 54$

$x =$ ☐

d. $\frac{y}{7} = 12$

$y =$ ☐

e. $1764 = k + 532$

$k =$ ☐

f. $22{,}100 = m - 620$

$m =$ ☐

g. $150 = 15p$

$p =$ ☐

h. $18 = \frac{c}{100}$

$c =$ ☐

2. Solve these equations.

a. $10 = q + 4.8$

$q =$ ☐

b. $r - 2.3 = 2.7$

$r =$ ☐

c. $10s = 1$

$s =$ ☐

d. $1.4 = \frac{t}{20}$

$t =$ ☐

3. Solve these equations.

a. $65 = x + 12 + 15$

$x =$ ☐

b. $h - 25 - 20 = 120$

$h =$ ☐

c. $s + 17 - 9 = 59$

$s =$ ☐

d. $1500 = f - 200 + 700$

$f =$ ☐

⚠ Solve problems

1. Match each expression to the correct meaning.

	subtract *y* from 3
3*y*	subtract 3 from *y*
y − 3	add 3 to *y*
y + 3	multiply *y* by 3
$\frac{y}{3}$	divide *y* by 3
	divide 3 by *y*

2. Toby has some toy figures (*f*). He loses 12 of them. He now has 29 toy figures left.

   a. Write this as an equation, using *f*. _____

   b. How many toy figures did Toby start with? ☐

3. A triangle has three angles as shown. The total of the angles is 180°.

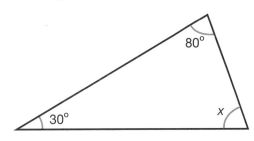

   a. Write this as an equation.

   _____

   b. What is the size of angle *x*? ☐

4. The perimeter of this irregular park field measures 1080m. The length of the shortest side (*y*) is missing.

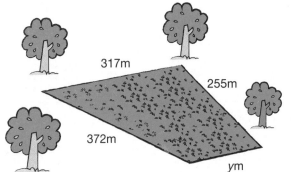

What is the length of the side *y* in metres?

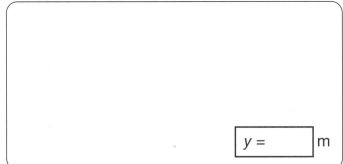

   y = ☐ m

8 More equations

○ Recap

In an equation, the values on the left-hand side must always be equal to the values on the right-hand side. We use letters to represent missing numbers. We 'solve' equations to find the value of the missing number.

$y + \cancel{8}_{-8} = 32$ To calculate y, start by subtracting 8 from the left-hand side of the equation.

$y = 32 - 8$ This means you must subtract 8 from the right-hand side too.

$y = 24$ Complete the calculation to solve the equation: y is 24.

If you do something to one side of an equation, you must do the same thing to the other side to balance it out.

📃 Learn

Some equations are more complex than the ones we have looked at so far. Here are some examples:

$3x + 7 = 19$ $8y - 46 = 34$ $\frac{z}{6} + 12 = 15$

In these cases, you will need to work through more than one stage before you can find the value of the letter.

$3x + 7 = 19$ To calculate x, start by subtracting 7 from the left-hand side of the equation.

$3x = 19 - 7$ This means you must subtract 7 from the right-hand side too.

$3x = 12$ We now know that $3x$ is 12.

$x \div 3 = 12$ Next divide the left-hand side by 3.

$x = 12 \div 3$ This means you must divide the right-hand side by 3 too.

$x = 4$ Complete the calculation to solve the equation: x is 4.

When you feel confident, you can shorten your working.

$8y - 46 = 34$ $8y = 80$ Add 46 to both sides of the equation.

                      $y = 10$ Divide both sides by 8 to solve the equation: y is 10.

$\frac{z}{6} + 12 = 15$ $\frac{z}{6} = 3$ Subtract 12 from both sides of the equation.

                      $z = 18$ Multiply both sides by 6 to solve the equation: z is 18.

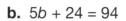

✔ Practice

1. Write down the calculations you need to do in the correct order. One has been done for you.

---

a. $4a - 11 = 25$

　　Add 11 to both sides.
　　Divide both sides by 4.

---

b. $5b + 24 = 94$

---

c. $\frac{m}{9} + 18 = 23$

---

d. $\frac{p}{12} - 5 = 6$

---

2. Now solve the equations in Question 1.

a.

b.

c.

d.

3. Write these equations as simply as possible but do not solve them. The first one has been done for you.

a. $2x + 7 + 3x + 8 = 100$　　$\underline{5x + 15 = 100}$

b. $y + 10 + 2y + 3 = 19$　　_____

c. $12t - 7t + 10 - 5 = 59$　　_____

d. $2r - 24 + r + 12 = 21$　　_____

4. Now solve these equations.

---

a. $2q + 4 - q + 13 = 25$

$q =$

---

b. $9b + 2 + b + 4 = 76$

$b =$

---

c. $k - 6 + 6k + 10 = 67$

$k =$

---

d. $h + 80 + 3h - 32 = 168$

$h =$

---

1. Wei thinks of a number (x). He divides the number by 4 and then adds 84. The answer is 100. What number did Wei start with?

   x =

2. Tamar buys 6 oranges. They cost z pence each. She also buys some apples for £1.50. She spends £4.50 in total.

   How much does each orange cost?

   z =   p

3. A rectangle has a perimeter of 60cm. The length of the longer side x is 23cm.

   x

   y

   a. Write the equation for finding the value of y. _____

   b. What is y in cm? Solve the equation. _____cm

4. Maria balances some pebbles on a set of scales. She puts the largest pebble on the left-hand side. On the right-hand side, she puts one large pebble and four smaller identical pebbles weighing p grams each.

   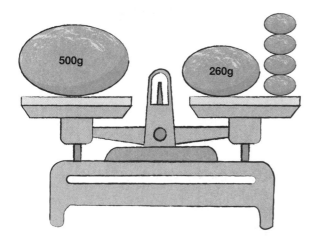

   500g

   260g

   How much does each of the smaller pebbles weigh?

   p =   g

9 Equations (two unknowns)

↻ Recap

In an equation, we can use a letter to represent an unknown number.

$$a - 15 = 70 \qquad 7x + 99 = 141 \qquad \frac{p}{10} - 50 = 5$$

We can solve equations in stages so that we isolate the letter and calculate its exact value.

$7x + \cancel{99} = 141$ $\scriptstyle -99$	We start by subtracting 99 from one side.
$7x = 141 - 99$	We must subtract 99 from the other side of the equation too.
$\cancel{7x} = 42$ $\scriptstyle \div 7$	We divide by 7 to isolate x on one side of the equation.
$x = 42 \div 7$	We must divide the other side by 7 too.
$x = 6$	We have solved the equation: x must equal 6.

📄 Learn

Equations can have more than one unknown value represented by different letters.

$$x + y = 20 \qquad a - 30 = b3 \qquad s + t = 100 \qquad \frac{k}{4} - 12 = j$$

Without further information, we can only work out the possible values of the letters (see pages 33 to 35). However, if we know the value of one of the letters, we can solve the equation in a similar way to calculate the other. Here are some examples:

Work out the value of x when $y = 6$.

$x + \underset{6}{\cancel{y}} = 20$	We start by substituting 6 for y.
$x + \underset{-6}{\cancel{6}} = 20$	To isolate x, we must subtract 6 from one side of the equation.
$x = 20 - 6$	We subtract 6 from the other side too.
$x = 14$	We have solved the equation: $x = 14$ when $y = 6$.

Work out the value of a when $b = 20$.

$a - 30 = \underset{20}{\cancel{b}}$	We start by substituting 20 for b.
$a - \underset{+30}{\cancel{30}} = 20$	To isolate a, we must add 30 to one side of the equation.
$a = 20 + 30$	We must add 30 to the other side too.
$a = 50$	We have solved the equation: $a = 50$ when $b = 20$.

1. Here is an equation: $x - y = 15$.

   Find the value of x when $y = 17$.

   > $x =$ ⬚

2. Here is an equation: $q + 210 = z$.

   Find the value of q when $z = 450$.

   > $q =$ ⬚

3. Here is an equation: $4m + j = 40$.

   a. Find the value of j when $m = 7$.

   > $j =$ ⬚

   b. Find the value of m when $j = 8$.

   > $m =$ ⬚

4. Here is an equation: $\frac{h}{3} - 9 = b$.

   a. Find the value of b when $h = 24$.

   > $b =$ ⬚

   b. Find the value of h when $b = 8$.

   > $h =$ ⬚

⚠ Solve problems

1. A cinema ticket costs £11 per person. There is also a booking fee of £2.50. Sam uses an equation to work out the cost of going to the cinema for different numbers of people. He uses p to represent the number of people and c to represent the total cost.

   $11p + 2.5 = c$

   a. How much does it cost for Sam and three friends to go to the cinema?

   £ ☐

   b. How many people go to the cinema if the total cost is £90.50?

   ☐ people

2. When $k = 12$, what is the value of v in the equation $v = 5k - 25$? ☐

3. Here is an equation: $2x - 5 = 3y + 8$.

   Find the value of x when $y = 9$.

   $x =$ ☐

4.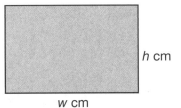

   h cm

   w cm

   The perimeter (p) of this rectangle can be calculated using this equation.

   $p = 2w + 2h$

   a. What is the length of side w if $h = 5.25$cm and $p = 24.5$cm?

   $w =$ ☐ cm

   The area (a) of this rectangle can be calculated using this equation.

   $a = wh$

   b. Use your answer to quesion 4a to calculate the area of the rectangle.

   $a =$ ☐ cm²

10 Possible numbers

⊃ Recap

Some equations have more than one unknown value. These unknown values are represented by different letters.

$$x + y = 6 \qquad b - 15 = c \qquad 2t + w = 16 \qquad \frac{j}{3} - 11 = m$$

If you are given the value of one of the letters, you can solve the equation.

Here's an example:

$x + y = 6$	What is x if $y = 2$?
$x + \underset{-2}{2} = 6$	To isolate x, you must subtract 2 from one side of the equation.
$x = 6 - 2$	You must subtract 2 from the other side too.
$x = 4$	You have solved the equation: $x = 4$ when $y = 2$.

Remember: You can only solve an equation with two unknowns when you are given a value for one of the letters.

🗐 Learn

Without further information, we can only work out the possible values of these letters, not exact values. In other words, there is more than one correct answer.

x and y each stand for whole numbers. Write a pair of numbers for x and y to make this equation true: $x + y = 6$.

$x =$ ☐ 4 and $y =$ ☐ 2 because $4 + 2 = 6$

Write down a different pair of numbers for x and y for the same equation.

$x =$ ☐ 1 and $y =$ ☐ 5 because $1 + 5 = 6$

Here's another example.

t and w each stand for whole numbers less than 10. Write a pair of numbers for t and w to make this equation true: $2t + w = 16$

$t =$ ☐ 5 and $w =$ ☐ 6 because $(2 \times 5) + 6 = 16$

Write down a different pair of numbers for x and y for the same equation.

$t =$ ☐ 4 and $w =$ ☐ 8 because $(2 \times 4) + 8 = 16$

1. $v + r = 15$

   a. Tick one pair of possible numbers for v and r from the choices below.

   9 ☐   7 ☐   6 ☐   5 ☐   8 ☐

   b. Now tick a different pair of possible numbers for v and r from the same choices.

   9 ☐   7 ☐   6 ☐   5 ☐   8 ☐

2. Circle the pair of whole numbers that make this equation true.

   $29 = e - f$

   56   20   12

   9   28   37

   41   48   50

   $e = $ ☐ and $f = $ ☐

3. For each of these equations, write down a possible pair of whole numbers that make the equation true.

   a. $p - g = 9$ $p = $ ☐ and $g = $ ☐

   b. $df = 24$ $d = $ ☐ and $f = $ ☐

   c. $\frac{m}{q} = 6$ $m = $ ☐ and $q = $ ☐

   d. $2j + b = 18$ $j = $ ☐ and $b = $ ☐

4. Write one pair of whole numbers less than 10 that make this equation true.

   $\frac{y}{4} = x$

   a. $y = $ ☐ and $x = $ ☐

   Now write a second pair of whole numbers less than 10 that make the equation true.

   b. $y = $ ☐ and $x = $ ☐

⚠ Solve problems

1. Lorenzo has a total of 28 pencils (p) and rubbers (r) in his pencil case.

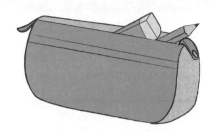

   He knows he has more than 20 pencils and fewer than five rubbers.

   a. Write a pair of possible values for p and r.　　　$p = \boxed{}$ and $r = \boxed{}$

   b. Write another pair of possible values for p and r.　　$p = \boxed{}$ and $r = \boxed{}$

2. Here is an equation: $xy = 32$.

   Which pair of numbers with the smallest difference between them makes this equation true?

   $x = \boxed{}$ and $y = \boxed{}$

3. There are three pairs of whole numbers less than 10 that make this equation true. What are they?

   $v + 3w = 20$

   a. $v = \boxed{}$ and $w = \boxed{}$

   b. $v = \boxed{}$ and $w = \boxed{}$

   c. $v = \boxed{}$ and $w = \boxed{}$

4. Here is a number machine:

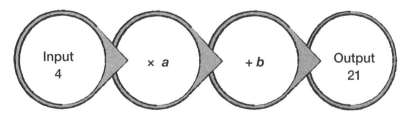

Input 4 → × a → + b → Output 21

   Write a pair of possible whole numbers where $a < 5$ and $b > 5$.

   $a = \boxed{}$ and $b = \boxed{}$

11 Word formulae

↻ Recap

The values on the left-hand side of an equation must always be equal to the values on the right-hand side. We use letters to represent one or more unknown numbers.

$$12 + 15 = 27 \qquad 14 = p + 10 \qquad f + y = 56$$

We can solve equations by isolating a letter. We can also work out the possible numbers when there is more than one unknown number.

$$14 = p + 10 \qquad \text{so } 14 - 10 = p \qquad \text{so } p = 4$$

$f + y = 56$ so f could possibly be 30 and y could possibly be 26.

Remember: An equation must balance. The equals sign is always at the balancing point.

📄 Learn

A formula is a type of equation. It is a bit like a mathematical recipe you can use to find an answer. A formula is often written using numbers or words or a mixture of both, but all are equations to be solved. Here is an example:

For adults, your maximum heart rate whilst exercising changes with age.

The formula for working out your maximum heart rate is:

Maximum heart rate in beats per minute (bpm) = 220 – your age

If Lola is 29 years old, we can use the formula to calculate:

$220 - 29 = 191$, so her maximum heart rate is 191 bpm.

Here is another example:

A shop sells muffins in boxes. Each muffin costs 50p and a box to carry them costs 30p.

The formula for working out the cost of one box of muffins is:

Cost = 50p × number of cakes + 30p for the box

If a customer buys 6 muffins we can use this formula to calculate:

$(50 \times 6) + 30 = 330$, so the cost is 330p or £3.30

1. Medhi bakes loaves, sticks and rolls every day.

    Tick the formula that expresses the total number of bread products he bakes each day.

    a. Number of loaves × numbers of sticks × number of rolls = total products ☐

    b. Number of loaves − numbers of sticks − number of rolls = total products ☐

    c. Number of loaves + numbers of sticks + number of rolls = total products ☐

2. There are 2.2 pounds in a kilogram.

    Tick the formula for converting kilograms to pounds.

    a. Pounds = kilograms × 2.2 ☐

    b. Pounds = 2.2 ÷ kilograms ☐

    c. Pounds = kilograms ÷ 2.2 ☐

3. Jayden sells clothes online. He charges £10 per item and a fixed charge of £2.50 for delivery.

    Write a word formula that expresses the price the customer pays for any number of items including delivery.

4. You multiply the width of a rectangle by its height to find its area.

    Write a word formula that expresses how to find the width of any rectangle from its area.

1.

The formula for working out how long to roast some meat is:
Total time = 40 minutes per kg + 20 minutes resting time

If the meat weighs 2.5kg, how long will it take to cook?

2.

Gus is converting kilometres to miles using this formula:
Kilometres = miles ÷ 5 × 8

How many kilometres are there in 70 miles?

km

3.

Michael is using a formula to calculate time on Mars:
Number of hours in a Martian year = number of hours in a Martian day × number of days in a Martian year

If there are 25 hours in a Martian day and there are 687 days in a Martian year, how many hours are there in a Martin year?

hours

4.

Kavi makes some sparkling orange juice using this formula:
Total quantity in ml = the quantity of orange juice + three times as much lemonade

If Kavi makes a total quantity of 340ml, how much lemonade does she use?

ml

12 Algebraic formulae

↻ Recap

A formula is a type of equation. It is a bit like a mathematical recipe you can use to find an answer. A formula is often written using numbers or words or a mixture of both.

A taxi charges £4.50 per ride and 25 per mile.

The formula for working out the fare is:

Fare = £4.50 + 25p per mile

Maria travels 20 miles in a single journey.
We can use the formula to calculate:

$450 + (25 \times 20) = 950$, so the fare is 950p or £9.50.

📄 Learn

A formula can also be written using algebra (numbers, letters and operations) instead of words. These formulae are called algebraic equations.

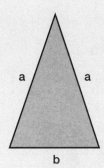

Here is an isosceles triangle.

The formula for calculating the perimeter (p) can be written as this algebraic equation:

$p = 2a + b$

If we know a = 6cm and b = 4cm then we can use this formula to calculate:

$p = (2 \times 6) + 4$, so the perimeter is 16cm.

Here is another example of a formula.

The price of a ticket for the zoo is £8 per student (s).
There is a discount of £3 on group bookings.

The formula for working out the cost (c) of a trip for any number of students can be written as the algebraic equation:

$8s - 3 = c$

If 10 students go on the trip, then then we can use this formula to calculate:

$(8 \times 10) - 3 = 77$, so the cost of the trip is £77 in total.

1. The area (*a*) of a rectangle is the product of its width (*w*) and height (*h*).

   Circle the correct formula for calculating the area.

   a. $a = w + h$ **b.** $a = 2w + 2h$ **c.** $a = wh$ **d.** $a = w - h$

2. Zahra counts some passing cars (*c*). She spots silver (*s*), orange (*o*) and white ones (*w*).

   Circle the correct formula for calculating the total number of cars.

   a. $= so + c$ **b.** $w = s + o + c$ **c.** $c = s + o - c$ **d.** $c = s + o + w$

3. The area (*a*) of a right-angle triangle is the product of its width (*w*) and height (*h*) divided by two.

   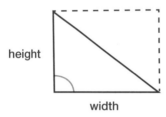

   Circle the correct formula for calculating the area.

   a. $a = \dfrac{wh}{2}$ **b.** $a = 2wh$ **c.** $a = w + h \div 2$ **d.** $a = w - h \times 2$

4. Write a formula that expresses this mathematical question.

   Hugo has ten T-shirts. He buys some more (*b*) and sells some others (*s*). How many T-shirts does he have (*t*)?

   _____

5. Write a formula that expresses this mathematical question.

   Olivia has some video games (*v*). Her cousin has three times as many games as Olivia. What is the total number of games (*g*) they have between them?

   _____

⚠ Solve problems

1. The internal angles *x*, *y* and *z* of a triangle add up to a total (*a*) of 180°. If angle *y* is 34° and angle *z* is 76°, what is angle *x*? Solve this question using the formula $x + y + z = a$.

$x =$ ___ °

2. Here is the formula for calculating the perimeter (*p*) of a regular hexagon.
   $p = 6s$ where *s* is the length of one side

   If the perimeter is 114cm, what is the length of one side?

   $s =$ ___ cm

3. Jamila is *j* years old. Her older brother is four years older than her. Jamila's younger brother is half the age of her older brother. If Jamila is 12, how old is her younger brother (*b*)? Use a formula.

   ___ years old

4. Two straight lines cross like this:

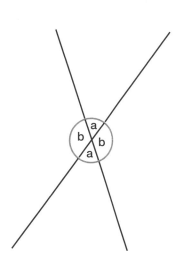

   The formula for working out the angles is $2a + 2b = 360°$

   Angle *a* is 29°. What is the size of angle *b*?

   $b =$ ___ °

Practice test 1 – Arithmetic

There are 20 questions in total, one mark per question.
Try to do the test in one sitting of 20 minutes.

1. $24 \div (50 - 44) =$ ☐

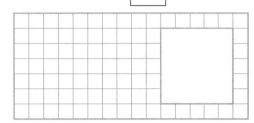

2. $7^2 \times 3 =$ ☐

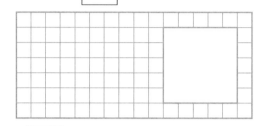

3. $6345 -$ ☐ $= 5039$

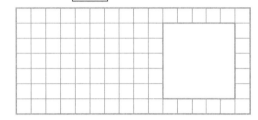

4. ☐ $+ 450 = 820$

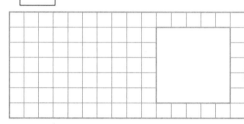

5. $84 - 56 \div 7 =$ ☐

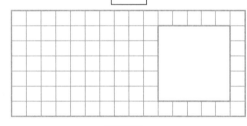

6. $6 \times$ ☐ $= 420$

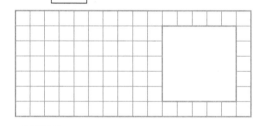

7. $3 + 9 \times 12 =$ ☐

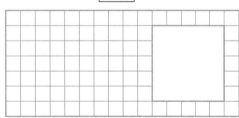

8. ☐ $- 100 = 2980$

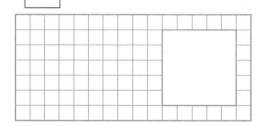

9. $90 - 2 \times 9 =$ ☐

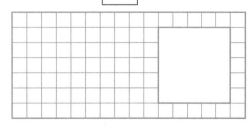

10. $600 \div (3 \times 40) =$ ☐

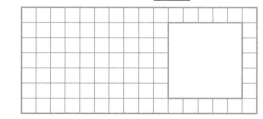

 1
 1
 1
 1
 1
 1
 1
 1
 1
 1

11. $6^2 + 30 - 6 =$ ☐

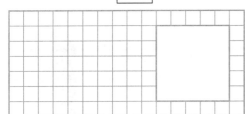

12. $(20 - 4^2) \times 8 =$ ☐

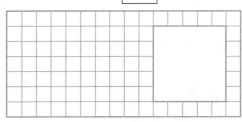

13. ☐ $+ 6 = 691$

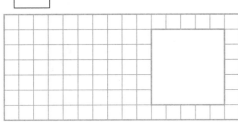

14. $60 \div$ ☐ $= 15$

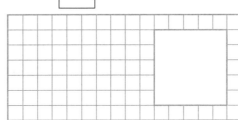

15. $72 + 72 \div 6 =$ ☐

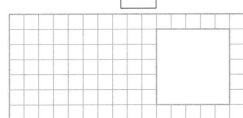

16. $3^2 \times$ ☐ $= 108$

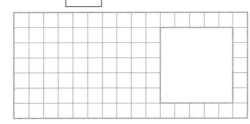

17. ☐ $- 120 + 30 = 250$

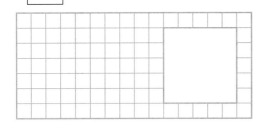

18. $60 \times (5^2 + 5) =$ ☐

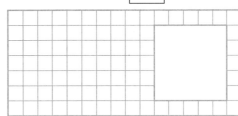

19. $100 - 9^2 =$ ☐

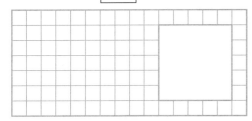

20. $(33 - 25)^2 =$ ☐

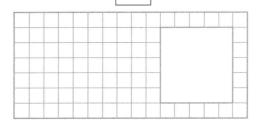

Practice test 2 – Reasoning

There are 12 questions in total, one mark per question.

Try to do the test in one sitting of 15 to 20 minutes.

1. Zainab has a bag containing four shapes.

   She pulls out two shapes. There are six different combinations.
   Zainab writes down five of them.

   triangle and circle   triangle and star   triangle and square

   circle and square   star and square

   Write the missing combination.

   _____ and _____

2. The rule to find the next number in this sequence is:
   'Double the number and then subtract 11'.

   Write the missing numbers.

	7		–5

3. Tom is saving some money. His parents offer to help him. They say,
   "For every pound you save, we will add half as much again."

   Which formula shows how much money Tom could save with his
   parents' help?

   n is the amount of money, in pounds, that Tom saves.

   Tick one.

   $n + 2n$ ☐

   $n + 0.5n$ ☐

   $2n + n$ ☐

   $n \times 2$ ☐

   $2n + 0.5n$ ☐

4. An ice cream parlour uses this formula to calculate the price of an ice-cream.

(60p × number of scoops) + (40p × number of toppings) + 75p

How much in pounds is an ice cream with three scoops and two toppings?

£ [＿＿＿＿]

1

5. and [▱] each stand for a different number.

What is the value of if = 9?

1

[＿＿]

6. x stands for a number.

x − 25 = 50

What is the value of x − 50?

1

[＿＿]

7. On a trip to a football match, each coach carries p passengers. Seven coaches make the journey, but three passengers miss their coach home.

   Write an expression for the number of passengers who return.

   ☐

8. y stands for a number.

   Complete this table of values.

$y =$	$2y + 8 =$	$y^2 - y =$
	18	

9. Join all the pairs of numbers that follow this rule:

   $p + 2q = 12$

   One has been done for you.

p	q
1	1
2	2
3	3
4	4
5	5
6	6

10. n stands for a whole number.

n^2 is greater than 5.

n^3 is less than 100.

What two numbers could n be?

☐ or ☐

1

11. Two rugs are the same length but with different patterns.

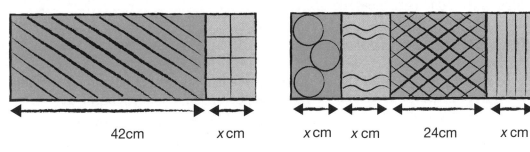

42cm x cm x cm x cm   24cm x cm

Calculate the length of each rug.

☐ cm

1

12. Here is an equation.

$y = 200 - 7x + 20$

What is the value of y when $x = 12$?

☐

1

Glossary

A

Algebra is the part of maths that uses letters and symbols as substitutes for numbers. It is used to find out the value of unknown numbers, and calculate using formulae.

> *$a = l \times w$: This formula is used to work out the area of a square or rectangle.*
>
> *$x - 10 = 50$: In this equation, x is unknown, but can be calculated.*

B

BIDMAS is an acronym that helps you to remember the rule for the order of operations in a calculation.

> *$7 \times (2 + 3) = 35$: This calculation has an addition in brackets and also a multiplication. In BIDMAS, B for brackets comes before M for multiplication, meaning, in this case, you must do the addition in the brackets before you multiply.*

E

Equation An equation is a mathematical statement that shows that two expressions are equal. The expressions are linked using the = sign.

> *$10 + 4 = 20 - 6$: Both expressions in this equation are equal in value (14).*

Expression A group of numbers, symbols and operators that have a value.

> *$8 + 3$ or $3x - 5$ or $a2 \times b2$*

F

Formula A formula is a rule written in symbols or words. It includes the = sign and two or more variables.

> *Area = length × width or $A = l \times w$: This formula is used to work out the area of a square or rectangle.*

I

Integer Any positive or negative whole number and zero. Integers are infinite.

> *−121 or 2987 or 0*

P

Pattern A sequence of numbers, shapes or symbols that repeats according to a rule.

> *aa, bb, cc, aa, bb, cc: This pattern is repeated pairs of letters.*

R

Rule A procedure for carrying out a process. A rule might be a formula or a way of describing a linear sequence.

> *3, 9, 27, 81, 243...: This sequence follows the rule 'Multiply by 3 each time'.*

S

Symbol A letter, numeral or other mark that represents a number, operation or mathematical idea.

> *x or y   often used to show unknowns or variables*
>
> *M   Roman symbol for 1000*
>
> *÷   divide*
>
> *∞   infinity*

U

Unknown An unknown is a number in an equation that is not yet known. It is represented by a letter.

> *$x - 10 = 50$: In this equation, x is unknown, but can be calculated.*

V

Value refers to how much something is worth in maths, such as an unknown number, a variable or the result of a calculation.

> *$2 \times 6 = 12$: the value of 2×6 is 12*
>
> *$x - 10 = 50$: the value of x is 60*

Variable A variable is a value that can change in an expression or equation. Letters are used to show variables.

> *$4x + 5$ or $2y - 3 = x$: In both cases, the values of x and y can vary.*